This book is for:

....

who is my best friend
in the whole world.

It was presented by me:

....

on the following date:

....

Written by Ellen Bailey, Ariane Durkin and Amy Wilson
Edited by Philippa Wingate
Designed by Zoe Quayle
Production by Joanne Rooke
Interior illustrations by Paul Middlewick and Zoe Quayle
Cover illustration by Paul Middlewick

First published in Great Britain in 2006 by Buster Books,
an imprint of Michael O'Mara Books Limited,
9 Lion Yard, Tremadoc Road,
London SW4 7NQ

Copyright © 2006 Buster Books

A CIP catalogue record for this book is available from the British Library.

ISBN-10: 1-905158-52-1
ISBN-13: 978-1-905158-52-2

2 4 6 8 10 9 7 5 3 1

Printed and bound in Italy by L.E.G.O.

Best Friends

Buster Books

Contents

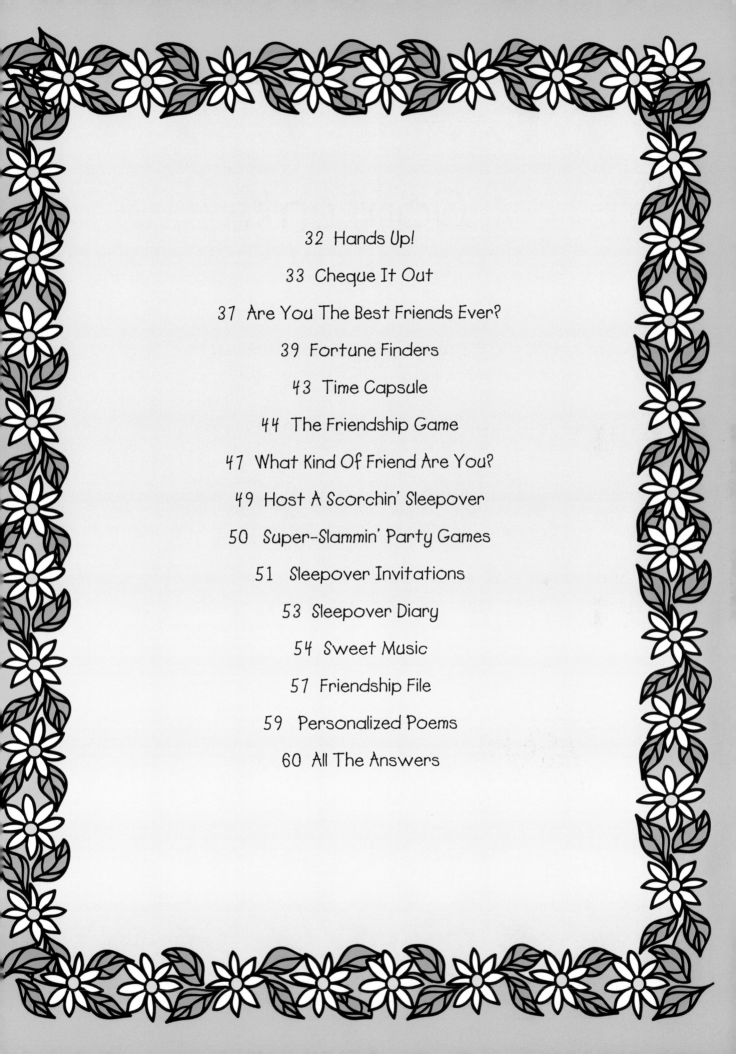

Best Friends
– An Introduction

Having a best friend (or a BF) is totally awesome. You know everything about each other – the good bits *and* the bad bits. You stick together through thick and thin. You talk on the phone for hours every night. You spend your weekends hitting the shops. And you never (well, almost never) fall out over that cute boy in class.

This book is designed to help you explore and celebrate your friendship. You and your BF will discover how well *you really* know each other, how compatible you are, and how to solve those friendship dilemmas and stay BFs for ever. Packed with revealing quizzes, sleepover games, great advice and the ultimate Rules of Friendship, this annual is guaranteed to help you fulfil your friendship potential. So grab your BF and get cracking!

Double Act Or Double Trouble?

Do you and your BF have the kind of friendship where you'd drop everything for each other? Together can you do things you wouldn't dare do alone?

Complete this quiz, then turn to page 60 to find out exactly what your answers mean.

1.

Your mate is grounded for the week. What do you do?

A) Spend the week talking on the telephone and making plans for the day she's released.
B) Sneak over when her parents' backs are turned and hole up in the bedroom to watch the latest DVD. It's a little naughty, but you're not doing any harm, surely . . .
C) Let her get on with her punishment and hit the cinema with some other friends. You'll see her at the weekend when her parents let her out again, and you know she would do the same if you were grounded.

2.

It's exam time. How do you and your BF study?

A) Hit the books together. Two minds are better than one, and you've always been good at helping each other to concentrate on the work in hand.
B) Each tell your parents you're studying at the other's house, then sneak out for some fun. Who's worried about exams anyway?
C) Hide yourselves away in your separate bedrooms for some serious revision – friendship will have to be put on hold for a week or so.

3.

Your friend is really upset. What do you do?

A) Make sure you're there for her at all hours – you know what it's like to be worried about something, and she's always there for you.
B) Take her out to the cinema, fill her with popcorn and cola, then send her home too tired to fret about anything. Talking about her problems for hours on end isn't going to achieve anything anyway.
C) Keep your distance for a while – she needs some space to work things out, and you're sure she'll be in touch when she's ready to come over for a girly night of face masks and music.

4.

It's Christmas and you want to treat your friend. What do you get her?

A) A picture frame with a photo of the pair of you inside, and a play list made especially for her.
B) That album she has been raving about and a huge poster of her favourite movie star, plus some little bits from the joke shop to make her laugh.
C) Bubble bath and a box of chocolates.

5.

You're at the cinema and the guy your best friend fancies is in the next row. What do you do?

A) Have a quiet giggle during the boring bits and tease her for looking over at him all the time.
B) Make people shuffle up so you can all sit together – you think his best mate is pretty cute anyway.
C) Try to watch the film while she passes notes to him. After all, there's plenty of time to talk to him when the film is over.

6.

You're both about to go on holiday and won't see each other for two weeks. What do you do?

A) Hit the shops together in preparation, and promise to text each other with news of any holiday romances.
B) Stage a protest and demand your parents go on holiday to the same place. Your little sister's just not as much fun as your BF.
C) Agree you'll send a postcard, and start daydreaming about all those bronzed hunks you're going to meet.

7.

You know before anyone else that your best friend fancies the new boy in class because ...

A) ... she has been looking at him out of the corner of her eye for days, and although nobody else would spot it, you can tell she's blushing when he talks to her. Even she might not know it yet – but she's smitten.
B) ... she keeps sending you messages about how cute he is, and you have been threatening to tell him. Of course you never would, but a bit of teasing never did any harm and she knows you're just pulling her leg.
C) ... you vaguely remember her saying something about somebody when you were on the way to the library.

8.

You're at a sleepover and someone begins teasing your best friend. What do you do?

A) Stand up for her. Nobody's teasing your best friend and getting away with it.
B) Join in, and make sure it's all good humoured. She's a good sport, and you know she would do the same thing.
C) Keep your mouth shut. It would just add to the embarrassment if you said anything.

9.

You're busily checking out the latest fashions at the shopping centre when your best friend realizes she's going to be late home. What do you do?

A) Rush home together and apologize, promising never to let it happen again. After all, if she's grounded you're not going to have much fun.
B) Get her to call home and tell her parents she's late because the bus left without you, even though you were there on time. It's not true, but how are they going to find that out? Besides, you don't want to stop shopping just yet!
C) Sympathize and see her to the bus stop, then whiz back to pick up that gorgeous little black number you've spotted.

10.

You're out for dinner and your best friend has ordered something awful by mistake. What happens next?

A) You share both dinners and enjoy the grimaces on each other's faces.
B) You kick up a fuss, insist her meal is inedible and ask the waiter for something different.
C) You pull sympathetic faces at your BF and dig in to your favourite spaghetti Bolognese. She should think more carefully before ordering.

Friendship Certificate

This is to certify that:

....

is my best friend in the whole world.
She is truly amazing. She makes me laugh when I'm stressed
out, and she understands that sometimes shopping is
the only way to cheer me up.

I hereby swear that I:

....

will be her best friend for ever. We will share each
other's secrets and each other's chocolate.
We will be honest, kind and considerate at all times.
Long live friendship!

Signed:

....

Ten Things I Love About My BF

There are thousands of things that
I love my BF for, but here are the top ten:

1. ....
2. ....
3. ....
4. ....
5. ....
6. ....
7. ....
8. ....
9. ....
10. ....

Signed:

....

Top Texting

Sometimes there's no time to chat. If you want to send a quick message to make an arrangement or your BF laugh, a snappy text is what you need. Here are some abbreviations, acronyms and emoticons that are essential for top texters everywhere.

2moro	tomorrow
2nite	tonight
ASAP	as soon as possible
BF	best friend
BFN	bye for now
F2T?	free to talk?
PCM!	please call me!
RUOK?	are you okay?
TMB	text me back
TTYL	talk to you later
W84Me	wait for me
Wan2Tlk?	want to talk?

If you want to make sure your best friend is feeling good, just send her a quick inspirational message that's bound to put a smile on her face.

(:-)URClvr	chill, you are clever
M:-)Yaslf	respect yourself
NvaGivUp	never give up
RFT***	reach for the stars
RmbaURA*	remember you are a star
Supa*	superstar
TOY	thinking of you
URAbFab	you are absolutely fabulous
URButifl	you are beautiful
URGr8	you are great
URMyBF	you are my best friend
URSoCool	you are so cool
XOXOXOXO	hugs and kisses

To avoid any misunderstandings, use the following emoticons to show your friend just how you feel.

:-)	I'm smiling or happy
;-)	I'm winking or joking
:-D	I'm laughing
:'-(	I'm crying
:'-D	I'm crying with laughter
:-(	I'm sad or disappointed
:-)))	ha ha ha
C=:-)	I'm laughing my head off
+-:-)	I'm dying with laughter
:-@	I'm shrieking with laughter

Keeping It Hush Hush

Secret languages are a must when you want to pass on important messages to your friends without anyone else getting in on the act. This guide shows several different ways you can keep things hush hush. If you and your best friend can become fluent in one of the codes below, you'll be able to have a whole conversation without anyone else understanding a word.

Pig Latin

This is a scorchingly simple way to confuse eavesdroppers. Just move the first letter of each word of your message to the end and add 'ay' to it.

For example: Hetay ewnay oybay siay osay orgeousgay.
Translates as: The new boy is so gorgeous.

Eggy-Peggy

This language can be a lifesaver if there's something you really need to get off your chest without anyone (apart from your best friend) finding out. Just add the word 'egg' in front of each vowel and pour your heart out.

For example: Eggi reggeeggally weggant teggo teggalk teggo yeggoeggu. Deggo yeggoeggu weggant teggo ceggomegge oeggvegger eggaftegger scheggoeggol? Translates as: I really want to talk to you. Do you want to come over after school?

Pen Puzzler

Here's a really radical way of passing cryptic notes. You will need a long strip of paper and two identical pens. Wind the paper tightly around one pen in a spiral from top to bottom. Write your message vertically down the pen (you may need to stick the paper with a bit of sellotape temporarily to stop it unwinding).

When you unwind the strip of paper, the message will be totally illegible. Only your best friend will be able to crack the code by wrapping the paper around her own pen. It's the real deal!

Morse Code

The oldies are the goldies. This code has been used for years all around the globe. It is very easy to use once you know how. In Morse Code each letter has a different combination of dots and dashes. Here's the alphabet:

A .-	**B** -...	**C** -.-.
D -..	**E** .	**F** ..-.
G --.	**H**	**I** ..
J .---	**K** -.-	**L** .-..
M --	**N** -.	**O** ---
P .--.	**Q** --.-	**R** .-.
S ...	**T** -	**U** ..-
V ...-	**W** .--	**X** -..-
Y -.--	**Z** --..	

To make things easier, write your message in code with a slash (/) between each letter. At the end of a word put a double slash (//).

For example: ..//....-/.-/-.-/-..//.---/---/....-/...//.-..//...//....-/...//.../....-/...//....-/...//....-/.../....-/...//
.../---/..-/.-./---//-.-./---//.-/...-/-.//...-/.-/---/...//-.-//.-./---//...//--./---/.-/---//-.-//..-//
---/..-/-/-/

Translates as: I heard Josh is going to ask you out.

Block Cipher

Start by writing your message in a rectangular box. Each row should have <u>seven</u> letters in it. For example, if you're telling your best friend that you're thinking of having a sleepover for your birthday, you could write:

```
I A M T H I N
K I N G O F H
A V I N G A S
L E E P O V E
R F O R M Y B
I R T H D A Y
```

To turn your message into block cipher, write down the letters as they appear in the vertical columns. For example, the above message would be written like this:

IKALRI AIVEFR MNIEOT TGNPRH HOGOMD IFAVYA NHSEBY

To decode a message, all your best friend has to do is write the words vertically in a box again. The number of letters in each coded word show her how many letters there are in a vertical column of the box.

Friendship Wordsearch

L	E	C	I	V	D	A	O	S	T	L	A
G	G	U	S	H	P	D	J	Q	Y	I	R
R	O	F	H	O	N	E	S	T	Y	F	L
E	Y	S	O	A	M	C	L	A	V	E	M
V	F	L	S	O	R	A	I	B	I	S	O
O	N	G	E	I	Y	P	S	G	C	A	G
P	L	Q	S	O	P	S	E	K	N	V	P
E	V	J	L	A	E	N	W	Y	T	E	E
E	N	G	S	H	U	R	E	H	F	R	A
L	C	O	L	I	F	S	A	O	A	N	V
S	I	L	N	S	C	O	V	H	P	W	J
G	A	E	L	T	R	U	S	T	V	S	P

Can you find the following friendship words hidden
in the grid above?

LOYALTY   LIFESAVER
TRUST   GOSSIP
HONESTY   SLEEPOVER
ADVICE   SHARE
GENUINE

16

The Business!

Here are some super-stylin' business cards to hand out to new friends. They will help you keep in touch *and* make sure your friends never forget your birthday!

CUT HERE

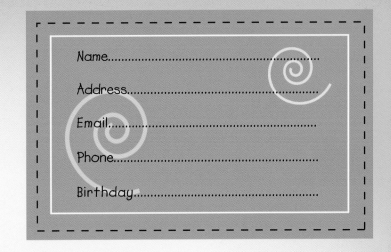

Name..
Address..
Email...
Phone...
Birthday...

Name..
Address..
Email...
Phone...
Birthday...

Name..
Address..
Email...
Phone...
Birthday...

Name..
Address..
Email...
Phone...
Birthday...

Name..
Address..
Email...
Phone...
Birthday...

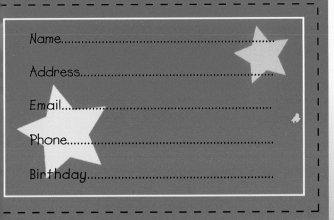

Name..
Address..
Email...
Phone...
Birthday...

Name..
Address..
Email...
Phone...
Birthday...

Let's hang out together soon!

Don't forget to call me!

Text me every day!

You are my friend for life!

You are totally cool!

Keep it real!

Never forget!

Friendship Dilemmas

When you have a best friend there's always somebody in your corner – somebody you can trust. But friendship isn't always plain sailing. Some things are difficult to deal with, but best friends can get through anything. It just takes time, patience and practice.

Here are some dilemmas you might face, and suggestions of how to deal with them to make sure you come through smiling together.

You've fallen out over the new girl

It's easy to get jealous when you see your best friend hanging with the totally elegant new girl. But remember, you two are officially the best friends ever. She's probably being kind, helping the new girl to settle in – one of the reasons you love her. Try to be friendly and welcoming yourself. Don't be hurt or get angry – explain to your BF that you feel a little vulnerable. She's sure to understand.

Your best friend is being bullied

Remind her that you will always be there for her. Tell her it's her friends who count, not the bullies. If the problem continues, encourage her to talk about it with her parents and teachers. Some problems are bigger than the both of you!

You find out you fancy the same boy

Talk about it. Half the class probably fancies him, so it might not be a really big problem. If he asks one of you out, you'll just have to make sure you tell each other everything. Keeping things secret from each other is the worst thing you can do. In the end, your friendship is more important than any cute guy. You never know – maybe he has an even cuter friend . . .

She's moving away

It's really hard when someone you care about leaves. But it does happen, and there's nothing either of you can do about it. So you have to make sure you stay in touch. Letters, emails and phone calls can be almost as good as seeing each other every day – it's quality time, not quantity! Make sure you keep each other in the loop with your lives. Think what fun it will be to check out her new turf, meet her new friends, and flaunt it down her new high street. Arrange to spend weekends together, so you can catch up with all the gossip.

It's her birthday and you can't make it to her party

If you've got to go to a family event or you're on holiday, make sure you let her know as soon as possible. Perhaps you could arrange a surprise pre-birthday treat at your house. Get some girls together, rent her favourite DVD and make sure she leaves smiling. She'll appreciate the gesture, and she'll get to celebrate her big day twice.

You've bought the same dress

Laugh about it and make sure you don't wear it on the same day. It just proves you both have a passion for fashion.

Body Language

Find out what your friend really thinks of you. Figure out her thoughts and opinions without her telling you a thing. All you have to do is observe her body language. Study her mannerisms, posture and facial expressions, and tick the boxes on the character cards below. Her every move will indicate her true feelings and state of mind.

Task One - Hands

Watch your best friend's hands. What does she do with them while you're talking to each other?

☐ *Does she drum her fingers on the table?* This is a clear indication that she is annoyed or frustrated by what you're saying. She is impatient and would like to change the subject.

☐ *Does she join her fingertips together to form a steeple?* This is a positive sign that your friend is listening and thinking about what you are saying. Forming a steeple shows that she is opinionated and confident.

☐ *Does she use her hands to cup her chin and rest her head?* Your friend is subtly telling you that she is bored. Alternatively, it could indicate she is tired and isn't too bothered by what you're saying.

Task Two - Sitting Position

Study the way your friend is sitting in her chair when at her school desk or while eating.

☐ *Does she sit with her legs stretched out in front of her and crossed at the ankles?* This may mean that she's feeling too shy to open up to those around her.

☐ *Does she have both her arms and legs folded at the same time?* This shows a lot of attitude. However, it may mean that she's putting up a front because she feels threatened or uncomfortable.

☐ *Does she lean her body towards you when she is talking?* Leaning forward while talking shows that she is paying attention and is interested in what you are saying. She feels confident confiding in you and trusts you completely.

Task Three - Eye Contact

Next time you are gossiping with your best friend, watch her eyes and make a note of where she's looking.

☐ *Does she make direct eye contact with you and rarely look away?* This means your friend is really listening to what you're saying. She's taking in the information you're giving her, and won't forget it all as soon as the conversation is over. However, some people may find her constant eye contact too intense and feel intimidated.

☐ *Does she hardly ever look into your eyes?* If you notice your friend always avoids eye contact, this may mean she's trying to hide something from you. Alternatively, it could mean she feels uncomfortable with what you are telling her.

☐ *Does she often stare at something in the distance?* She's not listening to you and is more interested in something else. Maybe she has just spotted a gorgeous boy behind you! She's just sooooo bored with the conversation.

Task Four - Stance

In the playground at lunchtime look at the way your mate is standing.

☐ *Does she stand with her weight balanced on both feet and her arms hanging loosely at her sides?* Your friend is comfortable in her own skin and glad to be with you.

☐ *Does she fold her arms and plant her feet close together?* This indicates she is tense and hostile. She's protecting herself, perhaps because she doesn't trust you.

☐ *Does she lean against a wall with her shoulders slouched and her head slightly tilted to one side?* Your mate is unhappy, but maybe not with you. The tilt of her head shows that she's preoccupied with something.

21

Body Flow

Go with the flow to find out what your mate's body language says about your friendship.

She's twiddling her thumbs or playing with a pen.

As you walk to the corner shop together, what do you notice about your friend's pace?

She walks in tandem with you.

start

You're gossiping about that fit boy in your science class, but what's your friend doing with her hands?

She walks much faster than you.

... partly covers her mouth with her hand.

She has both hands clasped together.

You ask for your best friend's opinion on your new outfit, but as she replies she ...

... gently scratches her ear lobe.

While you're waiting for the school bus, how does your friend stand?

With her arms dangling by her sides.

With both arms firmly crossed.

Great Mate
You've got the perfect mate! Your best friend's body language mirrors yours, which means she's relaxed and happy to be with you. If she gets upset about something, she'll speak up rather than cross her arms and huff and puff at you.

Frustrated Friend
Uh-oh! Have you done something to upset your friend? Her body language suggests she's not too happy. She's closing herself off from those around her and exuding a very hostile vibe. Tiptoe around her until her mood wears off.

You're hanging out with your best friend, watching TV. How does your mate sit?

A large distance away from you with her ankles crossed.

With her legs tucked beneath her and her hands resting in her lap.

Shy Sista
Shy is your best friend's middle name! She often feels uncomfortable in big crowds and is scared to be herself in front of others. However, you shouldn't take her timid behaviour personally – it's not that she doesn't like you, she's just not as bubbly as you.

When you talk to your best friend, where does she look?

She occasionally looks down at the ground.

Her gaze always strays away and focuses on other things.

Bored Buddy
Yawn! That's exactly how your friend feels right now. If you look at her subtle body movements, they tell you that she gets bored easily and has the attention span of a flea. She often forgets things, so don't be surprised if she misses your birthday!

The Rules Of Friendship

If you want the perfect friendship you have to earn it – and that means both of you! It's not easy to take the rough with the smooth, but if you stick to some basic rules of friendship you'll be laughing. Here are a few tips:

Honesty – If you aren't telling the truth, your friend will soon guess. Lying is just not an option.

Trust – Trust your best friend completely, and she will trust you. After all, what's the point in being best friends if you can't share your secrets?

Sense of humour – OK, so you're the best listener in the world, but sometimes it's good to let go of all those worries and just have a giggle.

Sensitivity – You might have the bubbliest best friend on the planet, but you still need to show her some TLC and understanding sometimes. Cut her some slack if she's blue – everybody has their off days.

Reliability – It might sound a bit boring, but if you keep standing her up or letting her down, there's no way your BF is going to stick around.

Focus – There's always lots going on, and boys can be very distracting, but if she's trying to tell you something make sure you always pay attention.

Loyalty – It's no good flouncing off with a new best friend every week. Nobody likes to be made to feel like a one-minute wonder.

Patience – Everybody has bad days, and if your best friend is annoying you, try to stay cool. After a couple of days you'll probably have completely forgotten what was bugging you.

Tact – If your best friend has done something really annoying then tell her about it, but do it calmly and rationally. Totally freaking out and screaming at her in public isn't going to do either of you any good.

Friendship Questionnaires

One of the most amazing things about having a best friend is that you know just about everything there is to know about each other. Find out whether you are soul sistas or just distant cousins by filling in the questionnaires on pages 24 to 27.

Turn the page, sit opposite each other, and each fill in one of the red questionnaires on pages 24 and 25. Put your name at the top and be honest about all the things you like and dislike. Absolutely no peeking and no copying – we know what you are like!

Then turn to the blue questionnaires on pages 26 and 27. Put your friend's name at the top and fill in the answers, imagining what she would answer. When you are finished, compare your answers and see which of you knows most about the other. You'll find out just how similar you are.

My Name is ....

My worst nightmare is ....

My favourite subject at school is ....

My favourite food is ....

The person I fancy at school is called ....

My favourite celebrity is ....

My worst fault is ....

My best quality is ....

My star sign is ....

My favourite animal is ....

My favourite teacher is ....

My favourite TV programme is ....

My dream holiday would be ....

I like spending my money on ....

The one thing that annoys me the most is ....

In five words I would describe myself as ....

My Name is ....

My worst nightmare is ....

My favourite subject at school is ....

My favourite food is ....

The person I fancy at school is called ....

My favourite celebrity is ....

My worst fault is ....

My best quality is ....

My star sign is ....

My favourite animal is ....

My favourite teacher is ....

My favourite TV programme is ....

My dream holiday would be ....

I like spending my money on ....

The one thing that annoys me the most is ....

In five words I would describe myself as ....

My Best Friend is ....

Her worst nightmare is ....

Her favourite subject at school is ....

Her favourite food is ....

The person she fancies at school is called ....

Her favourite celebrity is ....

Her worst fault is ....

Her best quality is ....

Her star sign is ....

Her favourite animal is ....

Her favourite teacher is ....

Her favourite TV programme is ....

Her dream holiday would be ....

She likes spending her money on ....

The one thing that annoys her the most is ....

In five words I would describe her as ....

28

My Best Friend is ....

Her worst nightmare is ....

Her favourite subject at school is ....

Her favourite food is ....

The person she fancies at school is called ....

Her favourite celebrity is ....

Her worst fault is ....

Her best quality is ....

Her star sign is ....

Her favourite animal is ....

Her favourite teacher is ....

Her favourite TV programme is ....

Her dream holiday would be ....

She likes spending her money on ....

The one thing that annoys her the most is ....

In five words I would describe her as ....

Ten Things You Should Say To Your BF . . .

1. You're my fashion icon! I love your sassy style.

2. You're the coolest chick on the dance floor.

3. I can trust you with my deepest secrets.

4. You always know how to cheer me up when I'm feeling down.

5. I love that you laugh at all my jokes, even when everyone else is groaning.

6. No one is as chilled as you are in a crisis. You are so much fun even when the pressure's on.

7. I love drooling over cute boys with you. You understand just how cool my crush is.

8. I'm lovin' just hanging out with you.

9. I know you will always be there to listen to me if I have a problem.

10. The only argument we have is over what flavour smoothie to make.

. . . And Ten Things You Should Never Say

1. You'd never fit into my new dress – no chance.

2. I can't remember the last time you had a good hair day.

3. I had no idea that was supposed to be a secret.

4. Was I supposed to call you last night? I completely forgot.

5. I'm going to the cinema with the new girl. We'll have to meet up another time.

6. I can't believe you like him – what a goofball!

7. Your house smells funny. Does your dad fart a lot?

8. You're such a bookworm, can't we do something a bit more exciting?

9. I'll come over so you can do my homework for me.

10. I'm sure he'll ask you out – eventually. Once he's asked out every other girl in the class.

Hands Up!

Look at the shape of and the lines on your friend's palms. Compare them to the pictures shown below to discover what kind of a mate she really is.

Earth Hand

Earth Hand

The Earth hand has a square palm with short, solid fingers and only a few strong lines on the palm. The Earth personality is practical, sensible and determined, and makes a really trustworthy, reliable friend.

Air Hand

Air Hand

The Air hand has a square palm with long fingers and a medium number of lines on the palm. The Air personality is lively, interesting, self-confident and probably the sort of friend who is full of exciting ideas for adventures and activities.

Water Hand

Water Hand

The Water hand has a long, oblong palm with delicate fingers and a large number of fine lines on the palm. The Water personality is artistic, dreamy and creative – a friend who is great at arts and crafts, and truly inspiring.

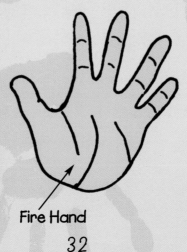

Fire Hand

Fire Hand

The Fire hand has an oblong palm with short fingers and many strong lines on the palm. The Fire personality is enthusiastic and sometimes a bit showy, with a real spark of magnetism. This makes for a fiery friendship, which might be full of furious arguments but will definitely be packed with excitement!

Cheque It Out

Cut out these sassy cheques, fill them in and pop them in the post to your best friend. They are a fabulous way of telling her just how much you care. Once you have signed on the dotted line you can't go back on your promise! But if you are really clever you could get her to fill one in and give it to you – guaranteeing you a gorgeous makeover.

Number 00001

Date...............

Payee..............

....

....

....

Bank of friendship

Valid from.................
to...........................

PAY...

I promise to stay up until

2a.m. at your sleepover

SIGNED: Your Best Friend

Number	Branch No.	Account No.	Sort Code
00001	09690	24370898	00-00-70

< **CUT HERE**

Number 00002

Date...............

Payee..............

....

....

....

Bank of friendship

Valid from.................
to...........................

PAY...

I promise to let you raid

my wardrobe

SIGNED: Your Best Friend

Number	Branch No.	Account No.	Sort Code
00002	09690	24370898	00-00-70

To.. (my best friend)

At..

....

....

Postcode............................

To.. (my best friend)

At..

....

....

Postcode............................

Cheque 1 (Number 00003)

Number 00003

Date...............

Payee.............

PAY...

I promise to hit the shops with

you this weekend

Bank of Friendship

Valid from..................

to..........................

Number 00003   Branch No. 09690   Account No. 24370898   Sort Code 00-00-70

SIGNED: Your Best Friend

Cheque 2 (Number 00004)

Number 00004

Date...............

Payee.............

PAY...

I promise you a girls' day out

Bank of Friendship

Valid from..................

to..........................

Number 00004   Branch No. 09690   Account No. 24370898   Sort Code 00-00-70

SIGNED: Your Best Friend

Cheque 3 (Number 00005)

Number 00005

Date...............

Payee.............

PAY...

I promise you a makeover

Bank of Friendship

Valid from..................

to..........................

Number 00005   Branch No. 09690   Account No. 24370898   Sort Code 00-00-70

SIGNED: Your Best Friend

To.. (my best friend)

At..

....

....

Postcode............................

To.. (my best friend)

At..

....

....

Postcode............................

To.. (my best friend)

At..

....

....

Postcode............................

Are You The Best Friends Ever?

OK, so you and your mate think you're the best friends ever, but what will this quiz reveal? Check out the answers on page 60.

1.

Your best friend is always late to meet you on the way to school and you get in trouble for it. What do you do?

A) Just deal with the trouble - you wouldn't want to risk the friendship over such a minor thing.
B) Explain to your friend that it upsets you and ask her to make an effort to be more punctual in future.
C) Get out of the problem by telling your friend that you've found a quicker route to school that's not on her way.
D) Teach her a lesson by telling everyone at school that the reason you're late is because she has to shave her moustache every morning.

2.

Eeek! Your best friend turns up at a party with a new haircut that is, like, totally last season. What do you do?

A) Put your hair up in a dodgy style so that she won't be the only one looking stupid.
B) Subtly suggest a way she could put it up that would help bring it up to date.
C) Ask the hostess of the party for a magazine, so that you can show your friend exactly where she went wrong.
D) Point and laugh at her.

3.

Your mate hasn't done her homework and asks to copy yours. Do you let her?

A) Of course. That's what friends are for.
B) Rather than let her copy, you quickly talk her through the exercise so that she can do it herself.
C) No, you'd both get in trouble if you were caught.
D) You haven't done yours either, so you'll have to find someone else's to copy.

4.

Your favourite TV show is just about to start and your best friend rings. What do you do?

A) Turn the telly off and have a good chinwag.
B) Berate her for calling, but end up missing the show because you've been laughing so much on the phone.
C) Shout at her and hang up, but call back when the show finishes.
D) Ignore the call and assume she'll call back if it's important.

5.

Your best friend's mum accuses her of something that was your fault. Do you own up?

A) No, she'd probably tell her mum before you had a chance to.
B) Definitely, and she'd do the same for you.
C) Maybe, if you thought she was really upset by it.
D) No way. If she's in trouble then it's her problem.

6. A new girl moves in next door to your best friend and they start spending a lot of time together. How do you react?

A) Phone your friend in tears and tell her you don't want to lose her.
B) If your friend rates her neighbour, the new girl must be pretty cool, so you suggest you all go shopping together.
C) Try to put your friend off the new girl by pointing out all her negative features.
D) Make sure the new girl knows she's not welcome by having a sleepover and not inviting her.

9. Your friend is trying on a dress and loves it, but you don't think it suits her. What do you do?

A) Nothing – she has great taste so you are sure she's right.
B) Tell her, and blame the dress for being badly cut.
C) Search the shops for a dress which really will suit her, and wean her off the other one by pointing out that it's too expensive anyway.
D) Let her buy it and hope you'll never be seen with her while she's wearing it.

7. What would you do if a nasty rumour about your best friend was going around the school?

A) Do everything you could to make sure she didn't find out.
B) Tell her about it. She'd prefer to hear it from a supportive friend.
C) Try to stick up for her by making up an equally horrid rumour about the girls that started it.
D) Laugh and join in – she'll see the funny side one day.

10. You ask to borrow your friend's top for the school disco, but she says no. What do you do?

A) Hit the shops and buy the same top for yourself.
B) Feel a bit upset but find something else to wear – you've got loads of great clothes so it's no big deal.
C) Sulk all day and vow never to let her borrow anything of yours again.
D) Say 'Duh! I was just kidding. As if I'd want to borrow *that* ugly thing!'

8. You've planned a trip to the cinema with your BF but you want to see different films. What do you do?

A) Agree to watch hers – you're really not that fussed.
B) Show her the rave reviews for your film to convince her, and promise that you'll go to hers next week.
C) Let her watch her film while you watch yours, then compare notes afterwards over a smoothie.
D) Bully her into seeing your movie – it's much funnier than hers anyway.

✂ **CUT HERE**

BLUE

5

You're always there to give reassurance and advice.

You really know how to listen to your best friend's problems.

9

RED

4

You really are the best friend anyone could have.

No one makes your best friend laugh like you do.

7

You can be two-faced. Don't betray your friends.

You are not afraid of being honest when asked your opinion.

3

8

YELLOW

Fair-weather friend! When the going gets tough, you get going.

You just can't be trusted to keep people's secrets.

2

1

GREEN

Fortune Finders

Find out how to fold a fortune finder on pages 38 and 39. Then, ask your BF to choose a colour from the outside flaps. Spell out the colour, opening and closing the fortune finder for each letter. Holding the fortune finder open, get your friend to pick one of the numbers shown inside. Count out the number. Get her to pick another number and count it out again. Ask her to pick a final number. Open up the flap beneath that number and read your friend's fortune.

Friend Or Foe? Friend Or Foe? Friend Or Foe? Friend
Or Foe? Friend Or Foe? Friend Or Foe? Friend Or Foe?
Friend Or Foe? Friend Or Foe? Friend Or Foe? Friend
Or Foe? Friend Or Foe? Friend Or Foe? Friend Or Foe?
Friend Or Foe? Friend Or Foe? Friend Or Foe? Friend
Or Foe? Friend Or Foe? Friend Or Foe? Friend Or Foe?
Friend Or Foe? Friend Or Foe? Friend Or Foe? Friend
Or Foe? Friend Or Foe? Friend Or Foe? Friend Or Foe?
Friend Or Foe? Friend Or Foe? Friend Or Foe? Friend
Or Foe? Friend Or Foe? Friend Or Foe? Friend Or Foe?
Friend Or Foe? Friend Or Foe? Friend Or Foe? Friend
Or Foe? Friend Or Foe? Friend Or Foe? Friend Or Foe?
Friend Or Foe? Friend Or Foe? Friend Or Foe? Friend
Or Foe? Friend Or Foe? Friend Or Foe? Friend Or Foe?
Friend Or Foe? Friend Or Foe? Friend Or Foe? Friend
Or Foe? Friend Or Foe? Friend Or Foe? Friend Or Foe?
Friend Or Foe? Friend Or Foe? Friend Or Foe? Friend
Or Foe? Friend Or Foe? Friend Or Foe? Friend Or Foe?
Friend Or Foe? Friend Or Foe? Friend Or Foe? Friend

Making Your Fortune Finder

1. Cut along the outer dotted line right around the fortune-finder sheet. Then fold one corner over to the other to make a triangle.

2. Fold your triangle in half again, to form a smaller triangle. Then unfold the sheet and lie it flat.

3. Fold each corner of the sheet into the middle, so the corners all meet at the centre of the sheet.

4. Turn the fortune finder over, and repeat step 3, folding the new corners into the middle.

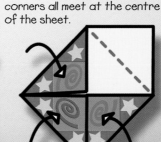

CUT HERE

BLUE

5

If you could look like anybody, who would it be?

Have you ever lied to your parents?

6

RED

4

Which boy in school do you fancy most?

Have you ever pretended to be sick to miss school?

7

3

If they made a movie about your life, who would play you?

Describe three things you like about yourself.

8

YELLOW

Which celebrity would you most like to meet?

Describe three of your faults.

2

1

GREEN

5. Fold the fortune finder in half from edge to edge, so the colour spirals remain on the outside.

6. Finally, unfold and fold in half the other way.

7. Slide the thumb and forefinger of both your hands under the flaps of your fortune finder.

Now you are ready to go!

41

Tell The Truth... Tell The Truth... Tell The Truth... Tell The
Truth... Tell The Truth... Tell The Truth... Tell The Truth...
Tell The Truth... Tell The Truth... Tell The Truth... Tell The
Truth... Tell The Truth... Tell The Truth... Tell The Truth...
Tell The Truth... Tell The Truth... Tell The Truth... Tell The
Truth... Tell The Truth... Tell The Truth... Tell The Truth...
Tell The Truth... Tell The Truth... Tell The Truth... Tell The
Truth... Tell The Truth... Tell The Truth... Tell The Truth...
Tell The Truth... Tell The Truth... Tell The Truth... Tell The
Truth... Tell The Truth... Tell The Truth... Tell The Truth...
Tell The Truth... Tell The Truth... Tell The Truth... Tell The
Truth... Tell The Truth... Tell The Truth... Tell The Truth...
Tell The Truth... Tell The Truth... Tell The Truth... Tell The
Truth... Tell The Truth... Tell The Truth... Tell The Truth...
Tell The Truth... Tell The Truth... Tell The Truth... Tell The
Truth... Tell The Truth... Tell The Truth... Tell The Truth...
Tell The Truth... Tell The Truth... Tell The Truth... Tell The
Truth... Tell The Truth... Tell The Truth... Tell The Truth...
Tell The Truth... Tell The Truth... Tell The Truth... Tell The
Truth... Tell The Truth... Tell The Truth... Tell The Truth...
Tell The Truth... Tell The Truth... Tell The Truth... Tell The

Time Capsule

Make a time capsule dedicated to your friendship, then fix a date way in the future to get together with your BF and open it up.

Will you still be into the same music? Will you have married your crush? Will your favourite outfit seem as funny as your mum's flares? A time capsule is a way of showing you are determined to stay friends for ever.

Find a biscuit or cake tin and line it with tissue paper to protect your treasures. Collect all the things listed below and put them in the tin. Fill in the questionnaires below (one each) and cut them out. Add personal items such as stickers, postcards or even a few of your favourite sweets - but remember not to put in anything that will go mouldy! Seal the tin and bury it.

A photo of you both in your favourite outfits.

Locks of your hair.

A CD of your favourite songs.

A picture of your crushes.

The front page of today's newspaper.

Self-portraits.

This week's issue of your favourite magazine.

A recorded message for the future you.

ate _____

ame_____

'hen I grow up, my job will be_____

definitely won't be _____

will live in _____

will be married to _____

will have _____ children.

Date _____

Name_____

When I grow up, my job will be_____

I definitely won't be _____

I will live in _____

I will be married to _____

I will have _____ children.

The Friendship Game

How well do you and your friends really know each other?
Play the Friendship Game to find out.

How To Play

1. Cut out the gamesheets opposite, turn them upside down so you can't see the different colours, then each choose one.

2. Fill in the questionnaires by ticking the answer that most suits your attitude. No cheating, ladies – tell the truth!

3. Fold the gamesheets and place them in a hat or lunch box. Give them a good mix-up and then each pick one. If anyone has picked their own, put them all back and try again.

4. Look over the gamesheet you've picked up and try to guess from the answers who filled it in. Write the name of the person you have guessed in the space at the bottom and then sign it.

5. Now show your sheet to the rest of the group. If you've guessed incorrectly, you'll have to make up for being such a lousy friend by doing the real author of the gamesheet the favour she chose in question 6!

44

1. To look this good for school each day takes me...
- ☐ ...a cool ten minutes.
- ☐ ...a happy half hour.
- ☐ ...sixty sassy minutes.
- ☐ ...two hours of boudoir bliss.

2. The number of people in our year that I've had a crush on is...
- ☐ ...urgh, zero.
- ☐ ...just the love of my life.
- ☐ ...sexy six.
- ☐ ...everyone!

3. The last time I lied to a teacher was...
- ☐ ...eek! Five minutes ago.
- ☐ ...last week.
- ☐ ...erm, over a month ago.
- ☐ ...in nursery school!

4. The thing that annoys me most about school is...
- ☐ ...that it's not the mall!
- ☐ ...mean teachers.
- ☐ ...dullsville homework.
- ☐ ...the ugly uniform.

5. When I finish school I'm heading...
- ☐ ...for uni life.
- ☐ ...to Bondi Beach.
- ☐ ...to a glam job.
- ☐ ...off on my honeymoon.

6. If my friend doesn't know these answers are mine, the favour I want her to do is...
- ☐ ...save me a seat in every class.
- ☐ ...get my school dinner and serve it to me at the table.
- ☐ ...carry my bag for the rest of the day.
- ☐ ...tell ten classmates how great I am.

I think this sheet belongs to _____

Signed _____

1. To look this good for school each day takes me...
- ☐ ...a cool ten minutes.
- ☐ ...a happy half hour.
- ☐ ...sixty sassy minutes.
- ☐ ...two hours of boudoir bliss.

2. The number of people in our year that I've had a crush on is...
- ☐ ...urgh, zero.
- ☐ ...just the love of my life.
- ☐ ...sexy six.
- ☐ ...everyone!

3. The last time I lied to a teacher was...
- ☐ ...eek! Five minutes ago.
- ☐ ...last week.
- ☐ ...erm, over a month ago.
- ☐ ...in nursery school!

4. The thing that annoys me most about school is...
- ☐ ...that it's not the mall!
- ☐ ...mean teachers.
- ☐ ...dullsville homework.
- ☐ ...the ugly uniform.

5. When I finish school I'm heading...
- ☐ ...for uni life.
- ☐ ...to Bondi Beach.
- ☐ ...to a glam job.
- ☐ ...off on my honeymoon.

6. If my friend doesn't know these answers are mine, the favour I want her to do is...
- ☐ ...save me a seat in every class.
- ☐ ...get my school dinner and serve it to me at the table.
- ☐ ...carry my bag for the rest of the day.
- ☐ ...tell ten classmates how great I am.

I think this sheet belongs to _____

Signed _____

1. To look this good for school each day takes me...
- ☐ ...a cool ten minutes.
- ☐ ...a happy half hour.
- ☐ ...sixty sassy minutes.
- ☐ ...two hours of boudoir bliss.

2. The number of people in our year that I've had a crush on is...
- ☐ ...urgh, zero.
- ☐ ...just the love of my life.
- ☐ ...sexy six.
- ☐ ...everyone!

3. The last time I lied to a teacher was...
- ☐ ...eek! Five minutes ago.
- ☐ ...last week.
- ☐ ...erm, over a month ago.
- ☐ ...in nursery school!

4. The thing that annoys me most about school is...
- ☐ ...that it's not the mall!
- ☐ ...mean teachers.
- ☐ ...dullsville homework.
- ☐ ...the ugly uniform.

5. When I finish school I'm heading...
- ☐ ...for uni life.
- ☐ ...to Bondi Beach.
- ☐ ...to a glam job.
- ☐ ...off on my honeymoon.

6. If my friend doesn't know these answers are mine, the favour I want her to do is...
- ☐ ...save me a seat in every class.
- ☐ ...get my school dinner and serve it to me at the table.
- ☐ ...carry my bag for the rest of the day.
- ☐ ...tell ten classmates how great I am.

I think this sheet belongs to _____

Signed _____

1. To look this good for school each day takes me...
- ☐ ...a cool ten minutes.
- ☐ ...a happy half hour.
- ☐ ...sixty sassy minutes.
- ☐ ...two hours of boudoir bliss.

2. The number of people in our year that I've had a crush on is...
- ☐ ...urgh, zero.
- ☐ ...just the love of my life.
- ☐ ...sexy six.
- ☐ ...everyone!

3. The last time I lied to a teacher was...
- ☐ ...eek! Five minutes ago.
- ☐ ...last week.
- ☐ ...erm, over a month ago.
- ☐ ...in nursery school!

4. The thing that annoys me most about school is...
- ☐ ...that it's not the mall!
- ☐ ...mean teachers.
- ☐ ...dullsville homework.
- ☐ ...the ugly uniform.

5. When I finish school I'm heading...
- ☐ ...for uni life.
- ☐ ...to Bondi Beach.
- ☐ ...to a glam job.
- ☐ ...off on my honeymoon.

6. If my friend doesn't know these answers are mine, the favour I want her to do is...
- ☐ ...save me a seat in every class.
- ☐ ...get my school dinner and serve it to me at the table.
- ☐ ...carry my bag for the rest of the day.
- ☐ ...tell ten classmates how great I am.

I think this sheet belongs to _____

Signed _____

46

What Kind Of Friend Are You?

Are you the person that your mate turns to when she's feeling down, or are you the one she calls when she's up for a party? When you have finished the quiz, find out what your answers mean on page 61.

2. You're hosting a sleepover. What kind of party do you throw?

A) Have loads of mates over for a super-slammin' party. It doesn't matter if you don't get a chance to talk to everyone - they know what you're like!
B) Chat until dawn with your best mate. You probably wouldn't even notice if nobody else turned up.
C) Invite a small group of close friends round and spend the evening watching films and doing each other's make-up.

1. Your BF comes to school looking blotchy and watery-eyed. How do you comfort her?

A) Make her laugh by doing impressions of the teacher.
B) Sit her down and make her 'fess up – a problem shared is a problem halved.
C) Take her to the bathroom, give her a big hug, and suggest you go shopping together after school.

3. You feel really hurt by something your best friend has said. What do you do?

A) Laugh it off. You're sure she didn't mean it really.
B) Call her up in tears and talk it over for an hour.
C) Explain to your friend that you're upset, then demand that she take you for a smoothie to make up for being so mean.

4. It's a gorgeous day outside and you head off with your best friend for a picnic. What do you take?

A) A frisbee, a radio and a towel (these things always end in a water fight).
B) A book, but you'll probably spend the time just having a good chat.
C) A magazine and some suntan lotion.

5. You're told off for not completing your homework on time. What do you do?

A) Say 'Homework? I thought that homework was meant to stay at home.'
B) Spend the day feeling really guilty and pledge never to hand it in late again.
C) Quickly do it at lunchtime so that you can hang out with your mates after school as planned.

8. There's a new girl at school. You like her, but your BF's not so sure. What do you do?

A) Get a group of mates together to go bowling, then subtly make sure your BF and new girl are on the same team - once they've got a few strikes between them they'll be like old friends.
B) Spend some time with the new girl, but reassure your BF that you're not dumping her.
C) Suggest you all go to the cinema together. Maybe if they spend some time with each other they'll realize how much they have in common.

6. Your best friend is ill. How do you help her recover?

A) Call her occasionally to check how she's doing, but hang with your other mates until she is back on the scene.
B) Go round every day after school to keep her up to date with all the latest gossip. Life really isn't the same without her.
C) Drop off a magazine, a bunch of flowers and a get-well-soon card.

9. Your best friend is having a sleepover, but you're not invited. What happens next?

A) You organize your own, way cooler, sleepover.
B) You send her a note asking what you've done to upset her.
C) You feel let down, but spend the evening pampering yourself and watching DVDs.

7. What is your favourite sort of TV programme?

A) A chart show with all the latest music, so you can check out what to play at your next party.
B) A good soap opera with characters you can really relate to.
C) Sitcoms.

10. At a party, your best friend's crush goes off with another girl. How do you console her?

A) You drag her to the dance floor and force her to boogie the night away.
B) You leave the party and go back to hers for a girly night. Who needs boys anyway?
C) You comfort her in the bathroom until she's ready to get back to the party.

Host A Scorchin' Sleepover

Invite all your pals over for a night of zingin' facials, kickin' fruit smoothies and the latest tunes. It's guaranteed to make you the most popular girl in town. Here's how to make sure your sleepover is a truly super-slammin' occasion for all duvet divas:

• Invite your friends in plenty of time, so that you can be sure they will be free on the night.

• If you're going to watch a DVD, chat to your mates about what they've seen and ask if there's anything new out that they fancy watching.

• Make a party mix with all your favourite tracks, so you don't waste time looking for them on the night.

• Let your friends know if there's anything you need them to bring. If you're planning a night of salon-style pampering, for example, this might include make-up, hair straighteners and everything you need for a facial and a manicure.

On The Night

Make sure you've got some tasty snacks and drinks in, then let your hair down and get ready for some serious boudoir bliss!

Sleepover Rules

1. Girls only.
2. Everyone must bring one thing that will make the sleepover more fun.
3. The host is DJ.
4. There will be a democratic vote for the choice of DVD.
5. There will be a feast at midnight.
6. Everyone must join in the fun – no wallflowers!
7. Secrets told at the sleepover must not leave the room.
8. Anyone who forgets their pyjamas must wear a silly nightie chosen by the host.
9. No snoring.
10. The host is in charge of breakfast.

Super-Slammin' Party Games

There's nothing better than chilling with good food and good friends at a sleepover. Make sure yours goes down in history with games and activities that are guaranteed to spice up the evening.

Spin The Bottle

An old favourite, Spin The Bottle is probably the giggliest game in history, and it couldn't be easier to play. Simply get an empty bottle and sit in a circle around it. Take turns to spin it. When it stops, the person towards whom the bottleneck is pointing has to complete a challenge, decided on by the rest of you. This might be a truth question about the person she fancies, or a challenge (such as eating three cream crackers in a minute), or a dare (such as running to the bottom of the garden in her nightie). Once the player has done what you've asked – or at least given it a good go! - she gets to spin the bottle to find the next victim.

Dance Moves

It's time to get groovilicious. If you can really shake your thang then why not spend the evening working out a dance routine to your favourite track?

Truth Or Dare

Get your mates to tell you all about their latest crushes, their most embarrassing moments, their dreams for the future and their worst habits - or make them suffer the consequences of keeping quiet!

Makeover

If you're all feeling the need for a little pampering, treat each other to manicures, pedicures and brand new hairstyles.

Chilling Stories

Take it in turns to make up scary stories. The person who gets the most spines tingling wins a prize.

Sleepover Invitation

It's Time To Get Out Your Pyjamas And Party!

I _____

Invite _____

To my sleepover on _____

At _____

Please bring _____

RSVP to _____

Can't wait to see you there!

Sleepover Invitation

It's Time To Get Out Your Pyjamas And Party!

I _____

Invite _____

To my sleepover on _____

At _____

Please bring _____

RSVP to _____

Can't wait to see you there!

CUT HERE

Sleepover Invitation

It's Time To Get Out Your Pyjamas And Party!

I _____

Invite _____

To my sleepover on _____

At _____

Please bring _____

RSVP to _____

Can't wait to see you there!

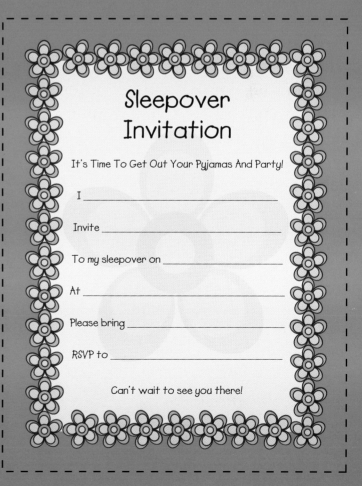

Sleepover Invitation

It's Time To Get Out Your Pyjamas And Party!

I _____

Invite _____

To my sleepover on _____

At _____

Please bring _____

RSVP to _____

Can't wait to see you there!

SLEEPOVER

SLEEPOVER

SLEEPOVER

SLEEPOVER

Sleepover Diary

Once you have hosted the perfect sleepover, you won't want to forget a single thing about it. Use this diary to keep a record of everything that happened.

Date of my sleepover _____

Who was there? _____

The games we played/things we did were _____

_____

The CD we played most was _____

The DVD we watched was _____

We ate _____

We drank _____

We got to sleep at _____

Rating out of 10: _____

Sweet Music

If you want to give your best friend a really thoughtful gift, make her a personalized CD cover so she can think of you when she's listening to her favourite tracks. Use the suggestions below to create a one-of-a-kind cover that she'll treasure.

• Make sure you're up to date on who her favourite bands and singers are, and cut out some pics of them from your old magazines.

• Next, choose your favourite photo of the two of you together. If you're very creative, you can also make it look as though she's snuggling up to her star crush!

• Add a photo or postcard of a place that's special to her, or tickets from a really cool gig or movie you saw together. You could press her favourite flower, paint her portrait or write her a poem (see page 59) to add to the cover. Anything goes!

• When you have your scorchin' selection of pictures sorted, glue them on to the covers opposite.

• Then fill in any remaining space with sequins, glitter or stickers to make it look really funky!

• Write a dedication especially for her.

• Finally, when it's dry, fit it into a CD case.

TITLE:

1 ....
2 ....
3 ....
4 ....
5 ....
6 ....
7 ....
8 ....
9 ....
10 ....
11 ....
12 ....
13 ....
14 ....
15 ....

To: ....
From: ....
Date: ....

TITLE:

1 ....
2 ....
3 ....
4 ....
5 ....
6 ....
7 ....
8 ....
9 ....
10 ....
11 ....
12 ....
13 ....
14 ....
15 ....

To: ....
From: ....
Date: ....

< CUT HERE

55

Friendship File

It's time to record the facts about your friendship. Fill out this page, and ask your BF to fill in the form on page 58.

My name is ___EMILEE PAIGE JOHNSON___

My birthday is on ___JUNE 21ST 1996___

My best friend is _____

We have been friends for _____ years.

We met at _____

We became best friends because _____

Our best day out was _____
_____

The kindest thing my BF ever did for me was _____
_____

Our worst quarrel was about _____
_____

We will be friends for _____ years.

Friendship File

This form is for your BF to complete.

My name is _____

My birthday is on _____

My best friend is _____

We have been friends for _____ years.

We met at _____

We became best friends because _____

Our best day out was _____

_____

The kindest thing my BF ever did for me was _____

_____

Our worst quarrel was about _____

_____

We will be friends for _____ years.

Personalized Poems

Writing a poem for your best friend shows you really appreciate her. There's nothing better than being given a personal poem. Use the letters of her name to give it an extraspecial twist. For example:

A Poem for Sophie

Some friends are just for good times
Others only help when you're sad.
Perfect friends are just like you
Honey, you're the best friend I've ever had.
In every way you're special to me
Exactly like a best friend should be.

Best Friend

Brightest star in the whole of the sky,
Each day I'm so happy we're friends.
So loving and kind, such fun to be with,
This friendship we've got will not end.

Facing things together makes it easy to
Ride the biggest waves and reach the stars.
In a magic world I'd fix it all so that
Everyone had friendships just like ours.
Now that I've finished I'd just like to say
Don't change, coz you're perfect this way.

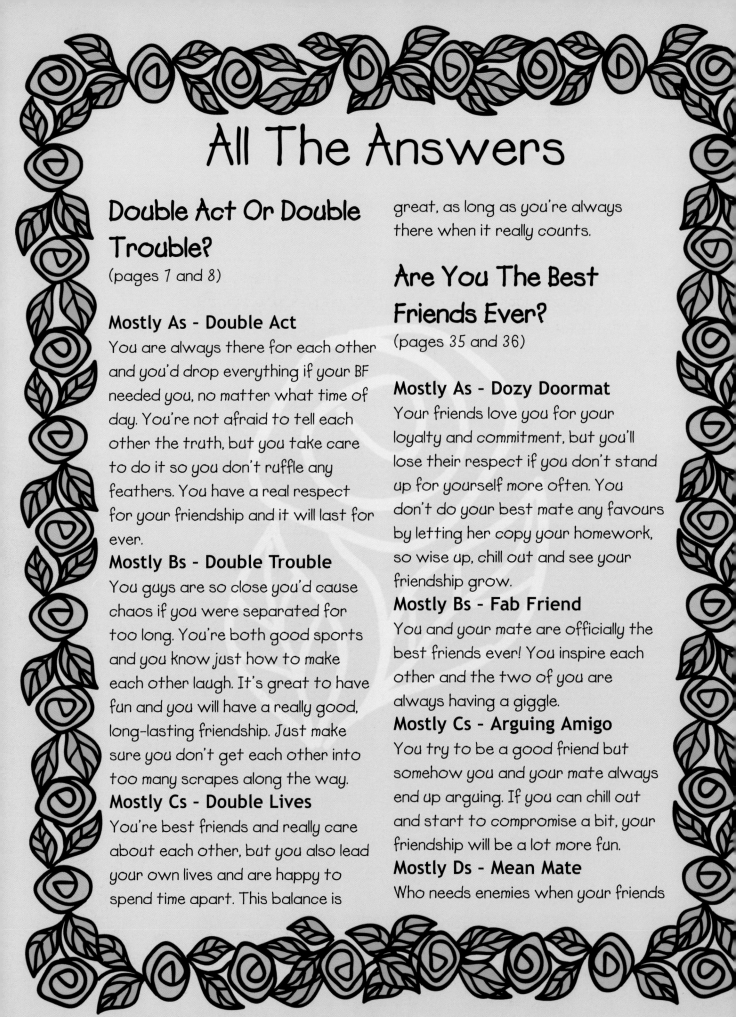

All The Answers

Double Act Or Double Trouble?

(pages 7 and 8)

Mostly As - Double Act

You are always there for each other and you'd drop everything if your BF needed you, no matter what time of day. You're not afraid to tell each other the truth, but you take care to do it so you don't ruffle any feathers. You have a real respect for your friendship and it will last for ever.

Mostly Bs - Double Trouble

You guys are so close you'd cause chaos if you were separated for too long. You're both good sports and you know just how to make each other laugh. It's great to have fun and you will have a really good, long-lasting friendship. Just make sure you don't get each other into too many scrapes along the way.

Mostly Cs - Double Lives

You're best friends and really care about each other, but you also lead your own lives and are happy to spend time apart. This balance is great, as long as you're always there when it really counts.

Are You The Best Friends Ever?

(pages 35 and 36)

Mostly As - Dozy Doormat

Your friends love you for your loyalty and commitment, but you'll lose their respect if you don't stand up for yourself more often. You don't do your best mate any favours by letting her copy your homework, so wise up, chill out and see your friendship grow.

Mostly Bs - Fab Friend

You and your mate are officially the best friends ever! You inspire each other and the two of you are always having a giggle.

Mostly Cs - Arguing Amigo

You try to be a good friend but somehow you and your mate always end up arguing. If you can chill out and start to compromise a bit, your friendship will be a lot more fun.

Mostly Ds - Mean Mate

Who needs enemies when your friends

have a mate like you? Does your best friend actually like you, or is she just too scared to tell it like it is? Putting your friends down is a sign of your own lack of self-esteem. If you start respecting other people, you'll soon get that respect back.

What Kind Of Friend Are You?

(pages 45 and 46)

Mostly As - Party Pal

You're great fun to be around and you're the first person your mates call if they're up for a party. You have loads of friends, but don't forget to take time out from all that partying to listen to their problems, as this will bring you even closer together.

Mostly Bs - Sympathetic Sista

You're a fantastic listener and would do anything to help a friend in need. Your mates all depend on you for a bit of TLC when they're feeling low, and you always say exactly the right thing to cheer

them up. Just don't forget to go out and party when the counselling session's over!

Mostly Cs - Great Mate

Not only are you always up for hitting the shops or going to a party, you're also there if your friend wants to spend hours analysing her crush's behaviour or moaning about her annoying stepdad. You're the kind of friend everybody needs - keep up the good work!

Friendship Wordsearch Answers

(page 14)

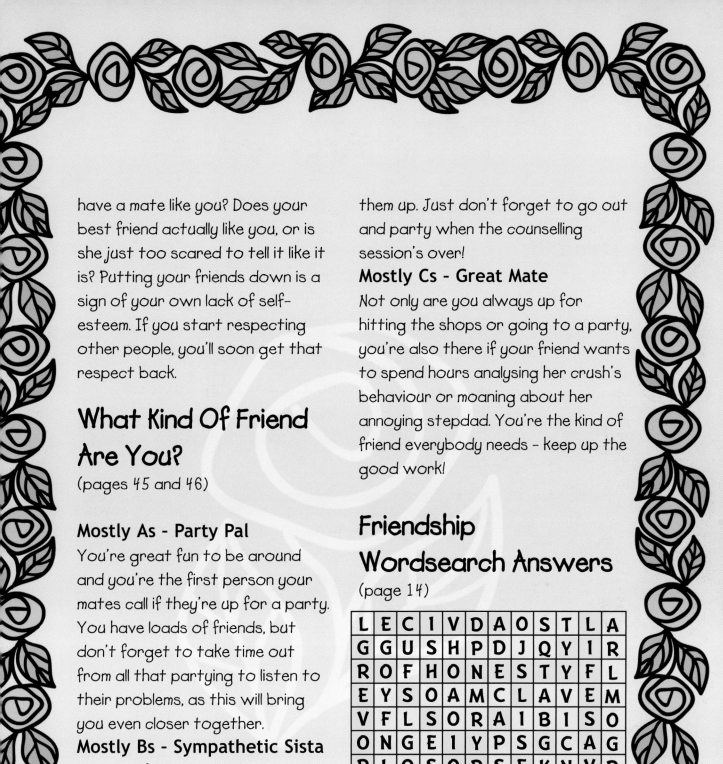

L	E	C	I	V	D	A	O	S	T	L	A
G	G	U	S	H	P	D	J	Q	Y	I	R
R	O	F	H	O	N	E	S	T	Y	F	L
E	Y	S	O	A	M	C	L	A	V	E	M
V	F	L	S	O	R	A	I	B	I	S	O
O	N	G	E	I	Y	P	S	G	C	A	G
P	L	Q	S	O	P	S	E	K	N	V	P
E	V	J	L	A	E	N	W	Y	T	E	E
E	N	G	S	H	U	R	E	H	F	R	A
L	C	O	L	I	F	S	A	O	A	N	V
S	I	L	N	S	C	O	V	H	P	W	J
G	A	E	L	T	R	U	S	T	V	S	P

61

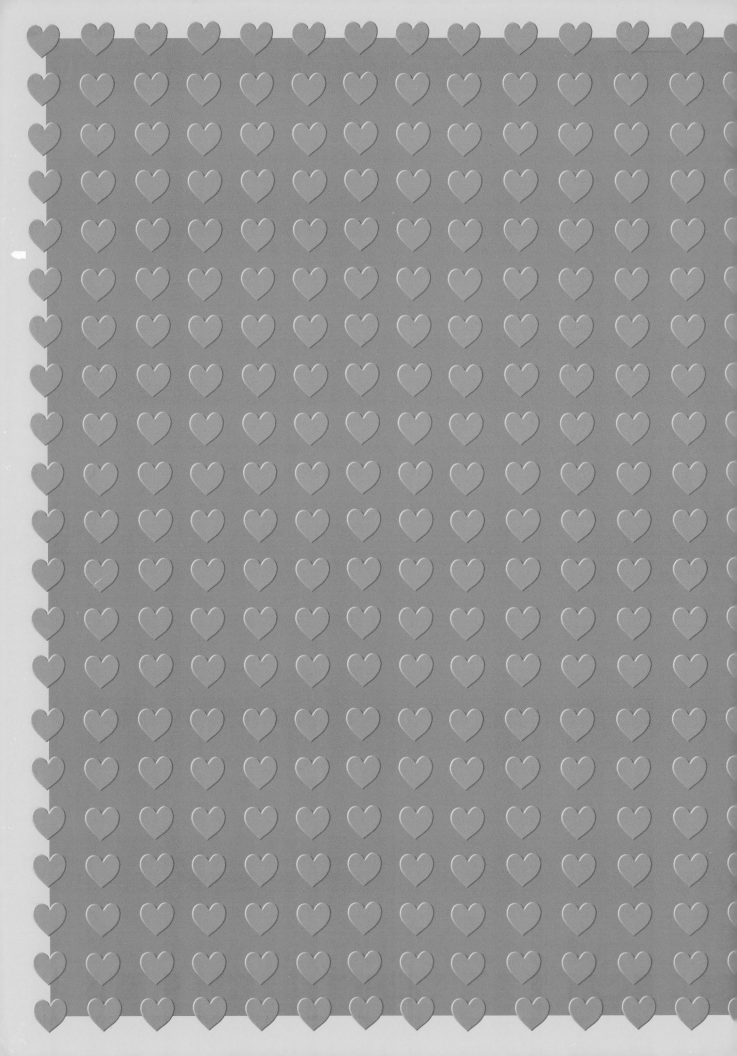